Horrid Henry's
Annual 2011

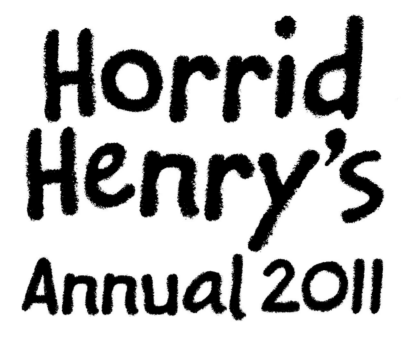

Horrid Henry's Annual 2011

Francesca Simon

Illustrated by Tony Ross

Orion
Children's Books

First published in Great Britain in 2010
by Orion Children's Books
a division of the Orion Publishing Group Ltd
Orion House
5 Upper Saint Martin's Lane
London WC2H 9EA
An Hachette UK Company

1 3 5 7 9 8 6 4 2

This compilation, *Horrid Henry's Annual 2011* © Orion Children's Books 2010
Design by Envy Design Ltd
Text © Francesca Simon 2010
Illustrations © Tony Ross 2010
Compiled by Sally Byford from the *Horrid Henry* books
by Francesca Simon & illustrated by Tony Ross

The Orion Publishing Group's policy is to use papers that are natural, renewable and recyclable
products and made from wood grown in sustainable forests. The logging and manufacturing processes
are expected to conform to the environmental regulations of the country of origin.

A catalogue record for this book is available from the British Library.

ISBN 978 1 4440 0088 7

Printed and bound in Italy

www.orionbooks.co.uk
www.horridhenry.co.uk

Contents

Hello Fans and Purple Hand Gang Members,

Welcome to my brand new 2011 Annual (I'm warning you Peter, this book is not for nappy faced toads; if you so much as peek inside it you will grow a second head...) Phew, that scared him off.

This time I'm going to tell *you* loads of top-secret stuff, stuff that Margaret would kill to know, stuff that would get me in so much trouble...but then, no mean horrible parents or smelly toad little brothers are going to find out, are they?

Nah nah ne nah nah!

Henry

How Many Pizza Slices?
There are pizza slices hidden throughout the Annual. How many can you find? Here's the first slice.

THE ONLY GOOD REASON TO GO SHOPPING

There will come a time when your **mean horrible parents** insist you have to go shopping with them for new school shoes or whatever. **BORING!** When they do, be prepared. Wait until they're exhausted then strike, and don't go home without **my best new favourites**. You'll find lists of them in my Annual. They're COOOOL!

BEST NEW BANDS

The Blobs
Zombie Cat Vampires
Hairball Jackals

Peter likes the Hip-Hop Hamsters. Bleccchhh! Believe me they are awful.

HOW TO AVOID GOING ON NATURE WALKS

- Have a **terrible tummy ache** (that is a sure-fire winner, just be careful you don't use this excuse when you want to do something fun a bit later, as your mean, horrible parents will probably make you stay at home).

- Complain about your **aching feet.** They wouldn't hurt so much if you had **Roller Bowler trainers.** More about these later!

- Tell your parents **you need to do homework.** (They'll never know you're reading comics in your room instead...)

- Throw a **tantrum.**

- Say you've heard that **terrible storms** are on the way and everyone is advised to stay indoors.

- If all else fails, say **you'll go next weekend** (a lot can happen between now and then, and hopefully they'll forget all about it...)

Horrid Henry's House of Fun

Most houses are really boring. That's because they're owned by boring grown-ups.

This is what *my* house will be like…

All food FREE.

MENU

The Worm's home

The Path of Life Maze

START

TIDY TED'S HOUSE

RUDE RALPH'S HOUSE

SWEET SHOP

GREEN GROCER'S

SKATE-BOARD PARK

LIBRARY

BOOK WORLD

FUN FAIR

Make your way through the maze and find out if you're following in Horrid Henry's footsteps or Perfect Peter's... But make sure you don't go round in circles!

You're Perfect!

You're Horrid!

Horrid Henry's Birthday Party

February was Horrid Henry's favourite month. His birthday was in February.

"It's my birthday soon!" said Henry every day after Christmas. "And my birthday party! Hurray!"

February was Horrid Henry's parents' least favourite month.

"It's Henry's birthday soon," said Dad, groaning.

"And his birthday party," said Mum, groaning even louder.

Every year they thought Henry's birthday parties could not get worse. But they always did.

Every year Henry's parents said they would never ever let Henry have a birthday party again. But every year they gave Henry one absolutely last final chance.

Henry had big plans for this year's party.

"I want to go to Lazer Zap," said Henry. He'd been to Lazer Zap for Tough Toby's party. They'd had a great time dressing up as spacemen and blasting each other in dark tunnels all afternoon.

"NO!" said Mum. "Too violent."

"I agree," said Dad.

"And too expensive," said Mum.

"I agree," said Dad.

There was a moment's silence.

"However," said Dad, "it does mean the party wouldn't be here."

Mum looked at Dad. Dad looked at Mum.

"How do I book?" said Mum.

"Hurray!" shrieked Henry. "Zap! Zap! Zap!"

Does Henry get his dream party? Find out in **'Horrid Henry's Birthday Party'** from **Horrid Henry and the Secret Club**.

Henry's Top Tips for the Perfect Party

HAPPY BIRTHDAY HENRY

1. PLACE

Get your parents to take you to Lazer Zap or a fantastic theme park. Say NO to the Fluffy Animals Farm or Princess World.

2. GUEST LIST

Invite as many people as possible. More people = more presents.

3. PRESENT LIST (VERY IMPORTANT)

Write a list and leave it for everyone to see, especially your parents because they've got loads of money.

4. FOOD

If your mum's list looks like this…

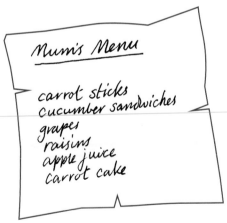

Mum's Menu

- *carrot sticks*
- *cucumber sandwiches*
- *grapes*
- *raisins*
- *apple juice*
- *carrot cake*

…bin it and write your own instead.

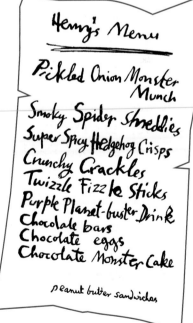

Henry's Menu

- *Pickled Onion Monster Munch*
- *Smoky Spider Shreddies*
- *Super Spicy Hedgehog Crisps*
- *Crunchy Crackles*
- *Twizzle Fizzle Sticks*
- *Purple Planet-buster Drink*
- *Chocolate bars*
- *Chocolate eggs*
- *Chocolate Monster Cake*

peanut butter sandwiches

5. PARTY BAGS

Fill them full of Chocolate Hairballs, Belcher Squelchers and Spiky Spiders, but make sure you've got plenty left to scoff later. Tell Mum NO granola bars, NO bookmarks, and DEFINITELY NO seedlings.

6. LITTLE BROTHERS AND SISTERS (MEGA-IMPORTANT)

Tell them they can't come to the party, but they do have to get you a present. Ha ha!

The Stinky Smelling Game

Here's the perfect game for Horrid Henry's birthday party!

You will need

5 different smells – see below for
some stinky suggestions
5 empty yogurt pots
Silver foil
Cocktail stick
A piece of paper and a pencil for
everyone playing the game

Stinky Suggestions

Vinegar   Used teabag
Tomato ketchup   Cheese
Lemon juice   Toothpaste
Chocolate   Shampoo
Coffee   Tinned tuna

Instructions

1. Before the party, put each of your different smells into a yogurt pot.

2. Cover the tops tightly with foil, and make a few holes in the foil with
   the cocktail stick.

3. Give everyone a piece of paper and a pencil, then pass round the yogurt pots,
   one at a time, for them to smell.

4. Ask your guests to write down what they think each smell is.

5. Reveal the stinky smells – the winner is the person who guesses
   the most smells correctly.

Horrid Henry Tricks Stuck-Up Steve

Stuck-Up Steve's bedroom is full of stuff Horrid Henry wants for himself. Henry hides five of Stuck-Up Steve's things – and waits to see if he notices. Take a good look at the objects on this page, then turn the page and see if you can work out which five are missing.

Can you work out which five objects Horrid Henry has hidden?

1. _____

2. _____

3. _____

4. _____

5. _____

April Fools' Day Maggots

Horrid Henry loves tricking his family and friends on April Fools' Day. Here's a really revolting trick he played on his mum.

You will need

Teaspoonful of cooked rice
Vegetable or olive oil
Small bowl
Apple

Instructions

1. Put the rice in the bowl, and stir in a small amount of oil – the rice will look really slimy!

2. Cut out a hole in the apple and push in the rice. Put the apple back in the fruit bowl, so that no one can see the rice.

3. Ask your mum if you can have an apple. She'll be delighted you want to eat some healthy fruit – tee hee.

4. Pick up the apple and pretend you're going to take a bite. Then yell very loudly, "Yeuch! It's full of maggots!"

5. Thrust the apple in your mum's hands. She'll scream even louder than you!

Moody Margaret's Make-up Tricks

Moody Margaret likes using her marvellous make-up skills on April Fools' Day.

Here are some of her favourite tricks.

Moody Measles

Cover your face, neck and any other parts of your body that are showing with bright red spots using face paint. Just remember – if you want this to work, DON'T WASH!

Too Tired to go to School

Sponge your face lightly with white face paint. Then dab a small amount of black face paint under your eyes. Look as weak and wormy as you can, and tell your parents you need to go back to bed to rest.

Big Bruise

Dab red face paint on a small area of your arm. Keep it light and uneven. When it's dry, use red face paint mixed with purple and sponge on a second layer in the middle of the bruise. Cry with pain when you show your parents – they might even give you some sweets!

Crazy Creatures

Horrid Henry often imagines he's a fire-breathing dragon burning his prey to a crisp or a coiling cobra about to strike.

If he could cast spells, he'd turn that goody-goody Peter into a beetle or a toad.

Why not turn yourself or someone you know into a crazy creature? You could copy one of the pictures on this page or draw a completely new creature.

Rude Ralph's Bouncing Easter Egg

Rude Ralph can make an egg bounce! Find out how he does it…

You will need

1 egg (raw)
Vinegar
A glass
Large bowl

Instructions

1. Fill the glass half full of vinegar and place the egg in the glass.

2. Leave it for seven days, then carefully take the egg out of the vinegar and put it into the bowl.

3. Pick up the egg, hold it about half a centimetre from the bottom of the bowl then gently drop it – and watch it bounce!

4. Try dropping the egg from a slightly higher height each time, until finally the thin rubbery shell breaks – SPLAT!

Nasty Nature Crossword

Henry's parents love a good walk in the springtime. But Henry knows the dangers of the great outdoors – fill in the crossword to find out what they are.

CLUES

ACROSS

1. Always close these behind you in the countryside – or you'll be followed by fierce beasts.
3. This wet stuff falls from the sky.
5. These little creatures poo on you from the sky.
7. Another word for 'hikes', but just as horrible.
8. Watch out for these scary quacking creatures.

DOWN

1. These greedy creatures will gobble anything!
2. The countryside is full of fearsome flocks of these animals.
4. Beware these plants – they sting.
5. If there's a sign saying, 'Beware of these animals', don't walk any further. Go home.
6. It's under your feet – and it's squelchy and dirty.

HORRID HENRY'S SECRET STUFF

HOW TO GET YOUR MEAN HORRIBLE LAZY PARENTS TO TAKE YOU TO A THEME PARK

Be careful here. Remember the awful time I won tickets to ... Book World, and had to practise checking out library books? So make sure it's **a REAL theme park**, with **scary rides** and **twirly whirlys** and **huge roller coasters** that whizz up and down and around so fast that everyone is sick and screaming.

- Beg every day to go.
- Beg every night to go.
- Tell your parents that everyone else has been.
- Tell your parents you need to go for a school project.
- Tell your parents that theme parks are educational.
- Tell them ... tell them .... tell them anything you like, just make sure you get there in the end!!!

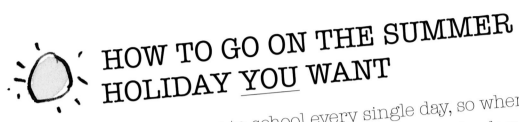

HOW TO GO ON THE SUMMER HOLIDAY <u>YOU</u> WANT

I heave my heavy bones to school every single day, so when it's **holiday time (yippee)** I want to relax, watch telly (check out Stuck in the Muck for hours of jaw-aching fun), eat crisps and **Not Move.** But my horrible parents like dragging me to boring places with little piles of stones that they say were castles once upon a time but are really just little piles of stones, or to museums, or to the seaside where there is freezing water and lots of sharks and slimy seaweed and sea monsters just waiting to swallow me up. **Ick. Yuck.** The best holidays mean relaxing indoors or only going outside to do what you want to do. **Here's how to make sure** these holidays are the ones you go on:

- Remind your parents how horrible last year's holiday was.
- Remind your parents how expensive last year's holiday was.
- Remind your parents about the time you threw up after the horrible holiday meal. And it was nothing to do with all the Chocolate Spitballs and Blobby Gobbers I'd been eating all day. Now that they remember, it's time to pounce!
- Suggest a theme park holiday.
- Keep suggesting a theme park holiday.
  - Don't forget, just keep suggesting a theme park holiday. They'll give in in the end.

Horrid Henry's Holiday

"We're going camping in France," said Henry's parents.

"Hooray!" said Henry.

"You're happy, Henry?" said Mum. Henry had never been happy about any holiday plans before.

"Oh yes," said Henry. Finally, finally, they were doing something good.

Henry knew all about camping from Moody Margaret. Margaret had been camping with her family. They had stayed in a big tent with comfy beds, a fridge, a cooker, a loo, a shower, a heated swimming pool, a disco and a great big giant TV with fifty-seven channels.

"Oh boy!" said Horrid Henry.

"Bonjour!" said Perfect Peter.

The great day arrived at last. Horrid Henry, Perfect Peter, Mum and Dad boarded the ferry for France.

Henry and Peter had never been on a boat before.

Henry jumped on and off the seats.

Peter did a lovely drawing.

The boat went up and down and up and down.

Henry ran back and forth between the aisles.

Peter pasted stickers in his notebook.

The boat went up and down and up and down.

Henry sat on a revolving chair and spun round.

Peter played with his puppets.

The boat went up and down and up and down.

Then Henry and Peter ate a big greasy lunch of sausages and chips in the café.

The boat went up and down, and up and down, and up and down.

Henry began to feel queasy.

Peter began to feel queasy.

Henry's face went green.

Peter's face went green.

"I think I'm going to be sick," said Henry, and threw up all over Mum.

"I think I'm going to be –" said Peter, and threw up all over Dad.

"Oh no," said Mum.

"Never mind," said Dad. "I just know this will be our best holiday ever."

Find out if Horrid Henry and his family enjoy their holiday in **'Horrid Henry's Holiday'** from **Horrid Henry**.

Horrid Henry's Survival Guide

There's nothing Henry likes better than lounging on the comfy black chair but he knows he's brave enough to survive in the toughest conditions if he has to. Follow in his fearless footsteps…

1. HOW TO MAKE A COMPASS

Exploring the Amazon or even just the jungle at the *bottom* of the garden, you'll be lost without a compass.

You will need

Bowl of water
Flat leaf
Sewing needle
Strong magnet

Instructions

1. Float the leaf on the surface of the water.

2. Hold the eye of the needle, and rub the sharp tip along the magnet sixty times. Always rub in the same direction, or your compass won't work.

3. Carefully place the needle on the leaf, then the leaf and the needle will turn so that the tip points North.

2. HOW TO MAKE A DEN

I sleep under the stars and listen to the wolves howling, but if you're not as brave as me, you'll need somewhere to hide.

You will need

A wall, a big rock or a tree trunk
Lots of branches and sticks

Instructions

1. Build your shelter against a solid base, like a fallen tree trunk, a rock or the shed wall.

2. Collect about ten long leafy branches and lean them up against your base so there's space for you to crawl under them.

3. Fill up the spaces with smaller branches, leaves, grass and moss.

4. Crawl into your cosy den – it's time for crisps and a fizzywizz drink!

3. HOW TO LEAVE A TRAIL

Everyone's read that soppy story about the children who leave a trail of crumbs through the forest. What a waste of a sandwich! If you get lost, find your way back home by following my simple signs made of sticks and stones:

Straight on   Turn right   Turn left   Don't go this way!   Gone home for tea

Horrid Henry Runs Away

When Henry runs away, it's his big chance to test out his survival skills.

Right, he thought, I'll only pack things I absolutely need. Lean and mean was the motto of Heroic Henry, Jungle Explorer.

Henry surveyed his room. What couldn't he live without?

He couldn't leave his Grisly Grub box and Dungeon Drink kit. Into the bag went the box and the kit. His SuperSoaker 2000 water blaster would definitely come in handy in the wild. And of course, lots of games in case he got bored fighting panthers.

Comics? Henry considered…definitely. He stuffed a big stack in his bag. A few packets of crisps and some sweets would be good. And the box of Day-Glo slime. Henry certainly didn't want Peter getting his sticky fingers on his precious slime. Mr Kill? Nah! Mr Kill wouldn't be any use where he was going.

Perfect, thought Henry. Then he closed the bulging case. It would not shut. Very reluctantly Henry took out one comic and his football. There, he thought. He'd be off at dawn. And wouldn't they be sorry.

Find out if Henry survives his adventure in **'Horrid Henry Runs Away'** from **Horrid Henry Gets Rich Quick**.

Survival Criss-cross

Below are some of the things that Horrid Henry needs to survive in the Wild.
Fit them into the criss-cross puzzle.

3 letters
MAP
HAT

5 letters
MONEY
TORCH
WATER
GAMES

6 letters
COMICS
SWEETS
CRISPS
STRING
JUMPER

7 letters
COMPASS

11 letters
SUPERSOAKER

CLUE:
Fill in the two longest
and the two shortest
words first.

The Big Summer Quiz

Can you answer Horrid Henry, Greedy Graham, Aerobic Al and Moody Margaret's questions about their special subjects?

GREEDY GRAHAM
Special Subject: Food

1. **Henry's parents promise to take him to Gobble and Go if he eats all his vegetables. What does Henry do with his sprouts to pretend that he's eaten them?**
   (a) He hides them in a drawer
   (b) He tucks them under the table
   (c) He puts them in his pocket

2. **When Horrid Henry dines at Restaurant Le Posh, what does he order?**
   (a) Tripe
   (b) Mussels
   (c) Snails

AEROBIC AL
Special Subject: Sport

3. **Who turns out to be a secret football fan?**
   (a) Mrs Oddbod
   (b) Miss Battle-Axe
   (c) Henry's mum

4 **Why does Perfect Peter get into trouble on School Sports' Day?**
   (a) He cheats at the sack race
   (b) He brings raw eggs for the egg and spoon race
   (c) He trips Goody-Goody Gordon over on purpose

**MOODY MARGARET
Special Subject:
The Queen**

5. When the Queen visits their school, who does Mrs Oddbod choose to present a bouquet?

(a) Horrid Henry

(b) Clever Clare

(c) Perfect Peter

6. What question does Horrid Henry ask the Queen?

(a) How many TVs have you got?

(b) How old are you?

(c) Do you like The Smelly Bellies?

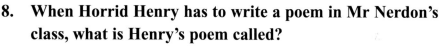

**HORRID HENRY
Special Subject:
Anything horrid**

7. What does Horrid Henry do to get out of having an injection at school?

(a) He cries

(b) He pretends to be ill

(c) He hides under a chair

8. When Horrid Henry has to write a poem in Mr Nerdon's class, what is Henry's poem called?

(a) I'm Gonna Throw Up

(b) Chips and Ice Cream

(c) My Little Brother is a Worm

How did you do? Check the answers on page 74.

6 – 8
What a big summer star you are! You're full of fascinating facts – and have obviously read lots of Horrid Henry books!

4 – 5
Smile! This is a sunny score!

1 – 3
Uh-oh! The sun isn't shining on you today. Try the Christmas Quiz instead!

Perfect Peter's Perplexing Puzzles

On long car journeys, Perfect Peter keeps busy with quiet pencil and paper puzzles. Here are some he drew for Henry to guess. Can you guess them too?

1. Which is the longest line?
A or B?
Answer _____

2. Which is the biggest inner circle?
A or B?
Answer _____

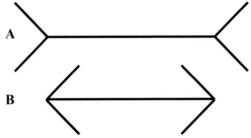

3. Which is the longest line?
A or B?
Answer _____

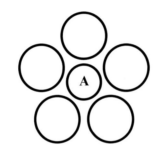

4. Which is the larger inside square –
The white square or the black square?
Answer: _____

Horrid Henry got them all wrong! How did you do?
Check the answers on page 74.

Horrid Henry's Noisy Car Games

Horrid Henry hates Perfect Peter's puzzles – especially when he scores a big fat zero. He prefers car games that make as much noise as possible!

HENRY'S NOISY ANIMAL GAME

When you drive past an animal, make the noise of that animal very loudly. The loudest person gets a point, and the first person to get ten points wins.

This is a brilliantly noisy game, and I'm the best player ever. Perfect Peter is rubbish.

HENRY'S NOISY DRUMMING GAME

Think of a song and beat out the tune on your legs or the window. Everyone else has to guess what the song is. The person who guesses the right answer gets to be the drummer.

My new favourite band is The Smelly Bellies because they're really noisy. I always choose one of their songs!

HENRY'S NOISIEST GAME

Everyone breathes in deeply and then makes a very loud noise for as long as they can. The person who can keep going the longest and the loudest is the winner.

Mum and Dad don't seem to like this game very much.

Aerobic Al's Silly Sports' Day

Aerobic Al takes School Sports' Day very seriously. But he also likes organising his own Silly Sports' Day for all his friends. Here are some of his crazy races.

AIR BALLOONS

Hand everyone a balloon, shout 'GO', and see who can keep their balloon up in the air for the longest.

AL'S RULES

- Don't catch or hold the balloon once it's up in the air.
- Never punch someone else's balloon to the ground.

HILARIOUS HOPPING

Take two long pieces of string (same length) and lie them on the ground like a wiggly path. The two people racing have to hop along the winding string.

AL'S RULES

- No pushing, shoving or tripping.

BALLOON RELAY

This is like a relay running race, but you have to run with a balloon gripped between your knees, and pass it on to the next person in your team.

AL'S RULES

- If you drop the balloon, go back to the beginning.
- If you touch the balloon with your hands, you're out.

Greedy Graham's Grub

ICE-CREAM IN A BAG

Greedy Graham loves ice-cream, not just in the summer, but all year round! Here's how to make your own scoop of soft vanilla ice-cream – in a bag. It's easy!

You will need:

Half a cup of full-fat milk
1 level tbsp sugar
¼ tsp vanilla essence
6 tbsps rock salt
2 self-seal sandwich bags (one inside the other)
2 large heavyweight plastic bags (one inside the other)
Lots of ice cubes (about 36)
Parcel tape

GREEDY GRAHAM'S TOP TIP – YOU MUST EAT THIS ICE-CREAM STRAIGHTAWAY!

Instructions:

1. Put the ice and the salt into the large bag.

2. Put the milk, vanilla essence and sugar into the small bag. Seal the bag, using parcel tape – to be extra safe!

3. Put the small bag into the large bag.

4. Gather up the top of the large bag in your hands, and shake it for about 6-7 minutes. Shake it outside or over the sink, in case of drips!

5. Open the small bag carefully, scoop out the ice-cream – and enjoy.

HOW NOT TO GO TO A MUSEUM

All the nature walk excuses work just as well for museums, but remember, museums are much better than nature walks, because **all museums have two great things: cafes and gift shops!** So if disaster strikes and your parents have dragged you kicking and screaming to some museum, don't lose hope. Follow signs to the Café and refuse to leave without some chocolate cake. Then head straight to the Gift Shop. With any luck you won't have to see anything but you can persuade your parents to buy you loads of cool stuff like Egyptian coffins and Roman coins.

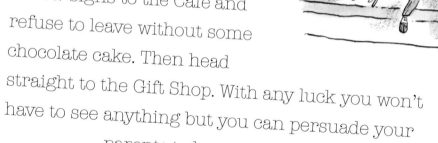

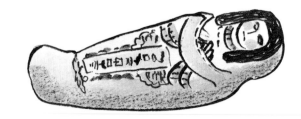

BEST NEW TV PROGRAMMES

Peter likes Cooking Cuties **(yuck)** but I try to grab the Comfy Black Chair first to watch Talent Tigers, **Knight Fight**, Terminator Gladiator and of course, my new favourite show ever, **Stuck in the Muck**

Miss Battle-Axe's Big Book

Whenever new teachers take Miss Battle-Axe's class, she hands them her Big Book full of pupil profiles – so they know exactly *what* and *who* to watch out for. Henry has sneaked a peek too and made a few small changes.

PUPIL PROFILES

KING **HENRY** THE HORRIBLE

This is all lies!
This boy is rude, lazy and disruptive. The worst student I have ever taught. If he says his homework has been eaten by the cat or hamster – do NOT believe him. You'd never believe his little brother is ~~such an asset to the school~~.
a pongy pants worm. Henry is the BEST.

MOODY **MARGARET**

bossy boots
Margaret is a ~~born leader~~ and likes to get her own way. She is a challenge to teach, but is destined ~~for success~~ when she grows up.
   to marry a toad

Margaret eats worms.

RUDE **RALPH**

Ralph is always too busy making rude noises to do any work. Do ~~NOT~~ let him sit next to Henry on the back row.

Ralph is lucky to have a brilliant friend like Henry.

44

PUPIL PROFILES

SOUR **SUSAN**

Susan is sour. She doesn't work hard in class because she is always whispering to her best friend, Margaret, or sulking because they have fallen out. Tee hee!

Susan is stupid
Susan is crabby

GREEDY **GRAHAM**

Graham always makes a big effort to get to lunch first. Be careful when you handle his homework – it's sometimes sticky.

Don't let Graham eat too many sweets. Make him give loads to Henry.

BEEFY **BERT**

Bert is quiet, but I'm not sure he's always listening and learning. He spends most of the lesson looking out of the window.

Because Miss Battle-Axe is BORING.

CLEVER **CLARE**

Clare is a delight to teach. A very clever girl. She hates giving wrong answers.

When there's a test, Henry must always be allowed to sit next to Clare.

Make Your Own School Newspaper

Why not write your own school newspaper with Horrid Henry's help?

Name Your Newspaper

I've already thought of the best name – *The Purple Hand Basher* – so you'll have to think of something else, nah nah ne nah nah. Moody Margaret's paper is *The Daily Dagger* – boring! – and Perfect Peter's is *The Best Boys' Busy Bee* – how smelly is that?

WRITE THE NAME OF YOUR NEWSPAPER HERE :

_____

Top Team

You could get some friends round to help you write your newspaper. But I do mine all myself because I'm brilliant. And I want to keep all the cold, hard cash I get when I sell millions of copies.

Headlines

Keep your headlines short and snappy. Here's one of my best *Basher* articles, with my most brilliant headline.

TEACHER IN TOILET TERROR

Terrible screams rang out from the boys' toilets yesterday. "Help! Help! There's a monster in the loo!" screamed the crazed teacher Miss Boudicca Battle-Axe. "It's got hairy scary claws and three heads!!"

What to put in your newspaper...

Write loads of good articles that people will want to read. Then they'll buy your paper and give you lots of money. You could write about...

- ## News

    Any exciting stuff going on at your school. If it's as boring as my school, do what I do – make it up!

- ## Sport

    Find out how the school teams are doing. I always include a few top tips for the teams in my paper, like – Hot-Foot Henry should be on the team – he's the best player in the school.

- ## Travel

    Write about school trips, like our trip to the Town Museum when Peter ended up in the Bad Children's Room, tee hee!

- ## Drama

    Review your School Christmas Play. Who was rubbish? (In mine, it was Peter – why did Miss Battle-Axe cast him as Joseph when he just squeaks like a squished toad?) Who was the star of the show?

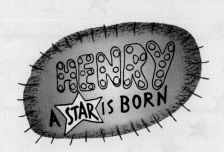

- ## Interviews

    I'm going to interview the demon dinner lady, Greasy Greta, and ask her why she's the sneakiest snatcher of all our sweets.

- ## Adverts

    Put an advert in your newspaper if you want to get rid of anything.

- ## Reviews

    Write about the best and worst TV programmes and give them stars out of 5, like this:

    MANNERS WITH MAGGIE – what a soppy programme – no stars

    KNIGHT FIGHT – the best programme in the whole world – 5 stars

Horrid Henry's New Teacher

The classroom door slammed. It was Mr Nerdon, the toughest, meanest, nastiest teacher in the school.

"SILENCE!" he said, glaring at them with his bulging eyes. "I don't want to hear a sound. I don't even want to hear anyone breathe."

The class held its breath.

"GOOD!" he growled. "I'm Mr Nerdon."

Henry snorted. What a stupid name.

"Nerd," he whispered to Ralph.

Rude Ralph giggled.

"Nerdy Nerd," whispered Horrid Henry, snickering.

Mr Nerdon walked up to Henry and jabbed his finger in his face.

"Quiet, you horrible boy!" said Mr Nerdon. "I've got my eye on you. Oh yes. I've heard about your other teachers. Bah! I'm made of stronger stuff. There will be no nonsense in my class."

We'll see about that, thought Henry.

"Our first sums for the year are on the board. Now get to work," ordered Mr Nerdon.

Horrid Henry had an idea.

Quickly he scribbled a note to Ralph.

> Ralph – I bet you that I can make Mr. Nerdon run screaming out of class by the end of lunchtime.
>
> No way, Henry
>
> If I do will you give me your new football?
>
> O.K. But if you don't, you have to give me your pound coin.
>
> O.K.

Find out if Horrid Henry manages to scare off Mr Nerdon in **'Horrid Henry's New Teacher'** from **Horrid Henry Tricks the Tooth Fairy**.

Ten Maddening Questions to Make Miss Battle-Axe Mad

Horrid Henry and Rude Ralph love annoying their teacher, Miss Battle-Axe. Here's a countdown of their ten most maddening questions.

10 My dad says, if you can't do it, teach it. Is that true?

9 Have you got rid of your nits yet?

8 Where did you buy that lovely cardigan?

7 Is it true you once met Queen Victoria?

6 Please could I have a copy of the worksheet for my invisible friend?

WARNING: Don't try these on your teacher!

5 Are you having a bad day, Miss?

4 Could you speak up, please?

3 Could you repeat the question? I wasn't listening.

2 Sorry, I don't understand. Could you start again from the beginning?

1 WHY?

Could You Turn Into a Teacher?

There aren't many things Horrid Henry thinks are worse than having Moody Margaret to stay, except for getting a horrible disease that turns you into a TEACHER.

Are YOU in danger of catching a deadly case of Teacher-itis?

1. Are you wearing any of the following?
(a) A saggy, baggy old cardigan
(b) Sensible, brown, lace-up shoes
(c) Neither of the above

2. If your friends are making lots of noise, what do you do?
(a) Shout "Shut up! I can't hear myself think" at them
(b) Try to think of a game that isn't so noisy
(c) Join in and make even more noise than them

3. How do you treat your little brothers and sisters?
(a) Tell them very firmly that, "small children should be seen and not heard"
(b) Encourage them with kind words, like "Well done" and "Aren't you clever?"
(c) Call them "worms" and ban them from joining any games

4. The house is a mess, but your parents are just watching TV. What do you do?

(a) Tell them that they're lazy, and the house is a disgrace

(b) Suggest that they finish all the housework first, and that their reward will be an hour of TV

(c) Sneak off when they're not looking, and make even more mess

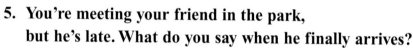

5. You're meeting your friend in the park, but he's late. What do you say when he finally arrives?

(a) What stupid excuse are you going to make up this time? Don't forget, I've heard them all before

(b) Where have you been? I've been waiting ages

(c) Have you got any sweets?

How to score:
For every (a) score 3 points; for every (b) score 2 points; for every (c) score 0 points.

ANSWERS

11 – 15

Uh-oh! You've caught the deadly disease and there's no cure. You're going to turn into a teacher – as grumpy and grouchy as Miss Battle-Axe.

5 – 10

Watch out! You're in the danger zone. Get help now – before it's too late.

1 – 4

Phew! You're safe from this horrible disease. There's no chance of your getting Teacher-itis!

Autumn Crossword

Perfect Peter enjoys long nature walks to look at the different coloured leaves in autumn. Henry prefers Halloween, bonfire night and throwing lots of leaves at Peter! Test your knowledge of autumn with this quick crossword.

CLUES
ACROSS

1. The fruit of an oak tree
5. A firework you can hold in your hand
6. The colour of hawthorn berries
7. A firework that spins round is called a Catherine _ _ _ _ _

DOWN

2. The fruit of a chestnut tree
3. Another sort of firework is a Roman _ _ _ _ _ _ _
4. Leaves can turn this colour in the Autumn

52

Horrid Henry
Tricks and Treats

Oh no. Horrid Henry felt as if he'd been punched in the stomach. Henry would be expected to go out trick or treating – with Peter! He, Henry, would have to walk around with a pink polka dot bunny. Everyone would see him. The shame of it! Rude Ralph would never stop teasing him. Moody Margaret would call him a bunny wunny. How could he play tricks on people with a pink polka dot bunny following him everywhere? He was ruined. His name would be a joke.

"You can't wear that," said Henry desperately.

"Yes I can," said Peter.

"I won't let you," said Henry.

Perfect Peter looked at Henry. "You're just jealous."

Grrr! Horrid Henry was about to tear that stupid costume off Peter when, suddenly, he had an idea.

It was painful.

It was humiliating.

But anything was better than having Peter prancing about in pink polka dots.

"Tell you what," said Henry, "just because I'm so nice I'll let you borrow my monster costume. You've always wanted to wear it."

"NO!" said Peter. "I want to be a bunny."

"But you're supposed to be scary for Hallowe'en," said Henry.

"I am scary," said Peter. "I'm going to bounce up to people and yell 'boo'."

"I can make you really scary, Peter," said Horrid Henry.

"How?" said Peter.

"Sit down and I'll show you." Henry patted his desk chair.

"What are you going to do?" said Peter suspiciously.

Find out what Horrid Henry does in **'Horrid Henry Tricks and Treats'** from *Horrid Henry and the Bogey Babysitter*.

Clever Clare's Magical Lava Lamp

Clever Clare has made her own colourful, erupting lava lamp. It's so easy – why not have a go?

You will need

Glass jar with a lid
Water
Food colouring
Glitter
Vegetable oil
Salt

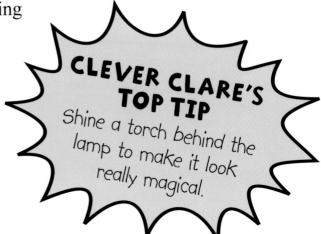

CLEVER CLARE'S TOP TIP
Shine a torch behind the lamp to make it look really magical.

Instructions

1. Fill the jar about three-quarters full with water.

2. Add a few drops of food colouring and add a teaspoon of glitter.

3. Fill the rest of the jar with vegetable oil.

4. Wait a few seconds until the water and oil have separated.

5. Add a teaspoon of salt to the jar – and watch what happens!

6. Whenever you want to make the lava erupt again – just add more salt.

Big Scary Phobias Wordsearch

On Halloween, you might suffer from WICCAPHOBIA (fear of witches) or PHASMOPHOBIA (fear of ghosts).

Find more weird and wonderful phobias in the wordsearch – the words are in the box below.

L	C	A	E	V	L	A	O	C	Y	J	A	O	S
A	A	L	I	W	A	I	Y	Q	Y	I	S	M	O
I	I	C	I	B	D	B	J	T	B	Q	L	P	M
B	F	G	H	N	O	O	J	O	O	X	E	H	N
O	Y	J	O	A	O	H	H	N	E	X	H	A	I
H	E	Q	M	C	N	P	P	R	V	I	P	L	P
P	H	U	C	K	O	O	H	O	P	Y	K	A	H
O	L	A	F	N	I	I	P	O	T	V	R	P	O
X	F	S	O	P	O	L	Z	H	B	U	I	H	B
Y	E	G	Z	T	I	B	O	C	O	I	L	O	I
M	O	Z	B	D	X	I	U	E	U	B	A	B	A
P	K	I	R	V	U	B	Y	S	P	J	I	I	A
B	U	F	O	N	O	P	H	O	B	I	A	A	X
A	I	B	O	H	P	I	C	E	L	O	C	S	A

Look up, down, forwards, backwards and diagonally

PHOBIA	FEAR OF…	PHOBIA	FEAR OF…
ABLUTOPHOBIA…..	washing	SOMNIPHOBIA……	sleep
BIBLIOPHOBIA…….	books	BUFONOPHOBIA…..	toads
CLINOPHOBIA……..	going to bed	OMPHALAPHOBIA…	belly buttons
POGONOPHOBIA…..	beards	SCOLECIPHOBIA…..	worms
LACHANOPHOBIA…	vegetables	MYXOPHOBIA……..	slime

Moody Margaret's Screaming Banshee Balloon

Moody Margaret loves scaring people on Halloween with her ear-piercing, screaming balloon.

You will need

Balloon
Plastic straw
Rubber band
Scissors

Instructions

1. Cut a 4cm piece from the plastic straw.

2. Push the straw inside the tube of the balloon. Leave 2cm sticking out of the end.

3. Wrap the rubber band around the straw and the balloon, so that the straw is securely fixed inside the balloon.

4. Blow the balloon up through the straw, then hold the straw tightly so the air doesn't escape.

5. Let go of the straw – and hold your hands over your ears!

SCREEEEEEEEEEEEEEECH!

56

Spooky Jokes Criss-cross

Match the words below to these well-known spooky jokes, then fit them into the criss-cross puzzle! One word has already been filled in.

**GUTS   BODY   NECK   MOUSE   BLOOD
COFFIN   SCREAM   CACKLE   TICKLERS**

Why didn't the skeleton cross the road?
He had no __ __ __ __

Why didn't the skeleton go to the party?
He had no __ __ __ __ to go with.

Which jokes do skeletons like?
Rib __ __ __ __ __ __ __ __

What's it like to be kissed by a vampire?
It's a pain in the __ __ __ __

When is it unlucky to see a black cat?
When you're a __ __ __ __ __ __

Why are graveyards so noisy?
Because of all the **C O F F I N**

What noise does witches' cereal make?
Snap, __ __ __ __ __ __ and pop.

What's Dracula's favourite soup?
__ __ __ __ __ __ of tomato.

Where do vampires keep their money?
In __ __ __ __ __ banks

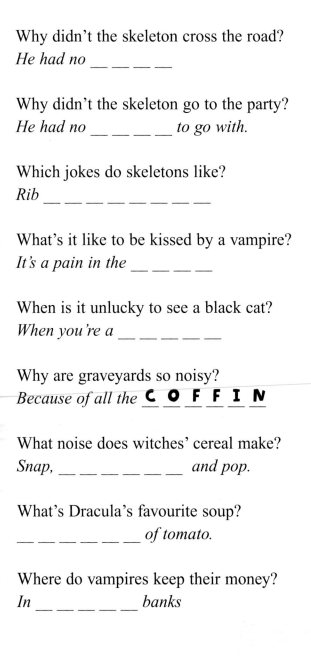

CLUE
Fill in the longest word first.

HORRID HENRY'S SECRET STUFF

HORRID HENRY'S BEST NEW SWEETS

Blobby gobbers

Rubber blubbers

Chocolate Spitballs

Fizzy Fizzers

Gooey Chewies

Peter's best sweets are Dew Drops, the no sugar, vegetable-flavoured treats. Ugh.

HORRID HENRY'S BEST NEW TOYS

Rabid Racer

Mini Madness

Strum N' Drum – it makes as much noise as ten bands playing at once!

Blaster Buzzers

PERFECT PETER'S BEST NEW TOYS

The Snoozie Whoozie, a bunny which giggles you to sleep

The Baa Baa sheep family

BEST TRAINERS:

Roller Bowlers, the trainers on wheels you can set to Screech; Fire-Engine; Drums, Canon, and Siren!!! You choose which noise you want the shoes to make, and the volume — **I like Sonic Boom best!**

I've told Mum and Dad, written to Father Christmas, written to Rich Aunt Ruby, so between all of them, someone should give me a pair!!! You can hear them from miles away.

Dotty Dominoes

Make your own Horrid Henry dominoes!
Start by cutting out twenty-eight paper or
cardboard dominoes, like this:

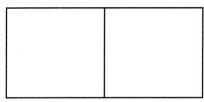

Choose six characters to draw on the dominoes – but make sure you include Henry and Miss Battle-Axe. If you choose Horrid Henry, Miss Battle-Axe, Rude Ralph, Beefy Bert, Moody Margaret, and Mum, you'll need:

A double of all the
characters, plus a
double blank
(7 dominoes)

Henry with Ralph,
Bert, Margaret,
Miss Battle-Axe
and Mum
(5 dominoes)

Ralph with Bert,
Margaret, Miss
Battle-Axe and
Mum
(4 dominoes)

Bert with
Margaret, Miss
Battle-Axe and
Mum
(3 dominoes)

Margaret with
Miss Battle-Axe
and Mum
(2 dominoes)

Miss Battle-Axe
with Mum
(1 domino)

All the
characters with
a blank
(6 dominoes)

Now it's time play dominoes – the Horrid Henry way!
1. Put all your dominoes face down on the table and
   muddle them up.
2. Each player takes seven dominoes. The player with the
   Horrid Henry double domino starts.
3. Now take it in turns to lay down a domino, matching one
   of your pictures to one already laid.
4. If you can't go, you have to pick up another domino
   from the table.
5. The first person to get rid of all their dominoes is
   the winner.
6. The loser is the person left with the most pictures of
   Miss Battle-Axe!

Brainy Brian's Cross-out Riddle-me-ree

Brainy Brian tells Beefy Bert that cats have more hair on one side than the other. But Beefy Bert can't work out which side of the cat is hairier. Follow the cross-out instructions and write the remaining letters in the spaces below to find out.

Cross out:

6 A's

7 B's

6 J's

5 K's

7 L's

5 M's

7 P's

7 X's

4 Z's

A	P	T	J	B	L	K	K
B	X	L	Z	H	X	A	M
E	M	X	J	P	L	P	B
M	K	Z	B	M	X	Z	O
J	P	U	A	T	B	J	P
S	K	X	L	M	J	I	L
A	L	B	X	D	P	A	B
P	X	E	J	A	K	L	Z

The hairiest side of a cat is:

___ _____

What's in Horrid Henry's Head?

Have you ever wondered what goes on in other people's heads?

This is what goes on inside of Horrid Henry's!

BEING HORRID

BUGLE BLAST BOOTS – I WANT THEM NOW!

PURPLE HAND – BEST CLUB EVER

HOW TO DEFEAT PERFECT PETER THE WORM

MUNCH 'N' CRUNCH

KNIGHT FIGHT – MY NEW FAVE T.V. PROGRAMME

OUTWITTING MOODY MARGARET

MONEY – HOW TO MAKE IT AND HOW TO SPEND IT

SMELLY BELLIES – BEST BAND

HOW TO GET OUT OF DOING CHORES

SWEETS – CHOCOLATE HAIRBALLS + SPIKY SPIDERS

SMELLY BELLIES GREATER HITS

Perfect Peter's brain is quite different!

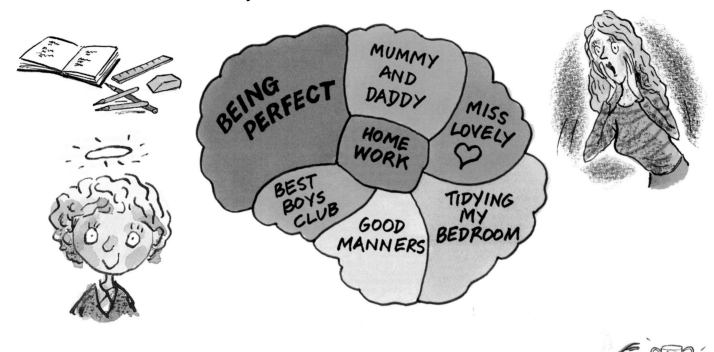

There's a great big section for being in moody in Moody Margaret's brain!

Why not have a go at creating your own brain? What would be inside yours?

Your Top Favourite Horrid Henry Book

In the last Annual, Horrid Henry fans were asked a very important question...

WHAT'S THE BEST HORRID HENRY BOOK EVER?

Fans emailed in their thousands to nominate their

Top Favourite Five-Star Most Brilliant Horrid Henry book.

The votes were counted – and the top three books are:

3rd – Horrid Henry Gets Rich Quick

2nd – Horrid Henry's Underpants

1st – Horrid Henry Tricks the Tooth Fairy

Here's an extract from your favourite:

> Henry dashed to the cupboard where Mum kept the sweet jar. Sweet day was Saturday, and today was Thursday. Two whole days before he got into trouble.
>
> Henry stuffed as many sticky sweets into his mouth as fast as he could.
>
> Chomp Chomp Chomp Chomp.
>
> Chomp Chew Chomp Chew.
>
> Chompa Chew Chompa Chew
>
> Chompa … Chompa … Chompa … Chompa … Chew.
>
> Henry's jaw started to slow down. He put the last sticky toffee in his mouth and forced his teeth to move up and down.
>
> Henry started to feel sick. His teeth felt even sicker. He wiggled them hopefully. After all that sugar one was sure to fall out. He could see all the comics he would buy with his pound already.
>
> Henry wiggled his teeth again. And again.
>
> Nothing moved.
>
> Rats, thought Henry. His mouth hurt. His gums hurt. His tummy hurt. What did a boy have to do to get a tooth?
>
> Then Henry had a wonderful, spectacular idea.

Spot the Difference

Look carefully at the two pictures and spot the six differences.

1. _____

2. _____

3. _____

4. _____

5. _____

6. _____

Best Friends

Who's your ideal best friend – Horrid Henry, Moody Margaret or Perfect Peter?

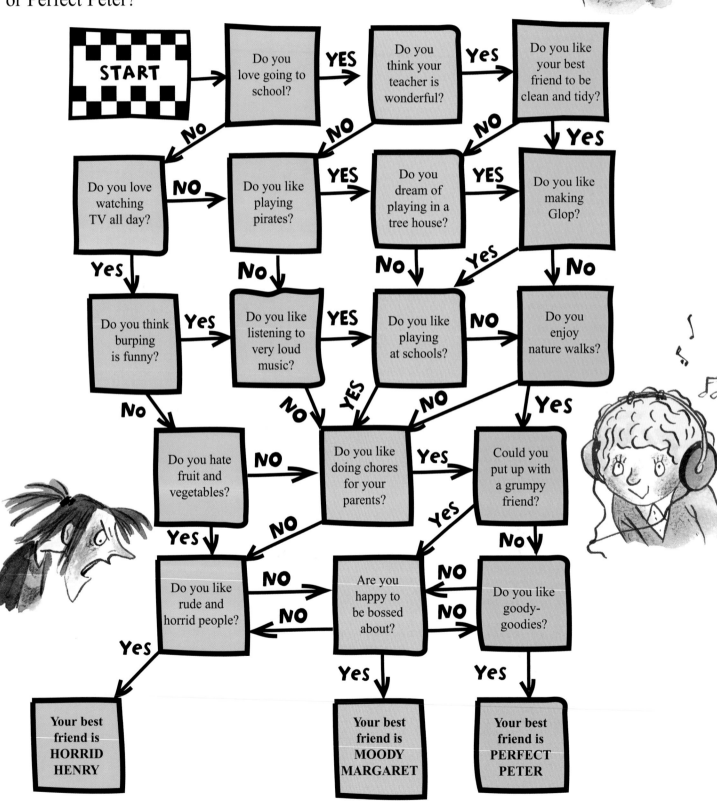

START

Do you love going to school? — **YES** → Do you think your teacher is wonderful? — **Yes** → Do you like your best friend to be clean and tidy?

Do you love going to school? — **NO** → Do you love watching TV all day?

Do you think your teacher is wonderful? — **NO** → Do you like playing pirates?

Do you like your best friend to be clean and tidy? — **Yes** → Do you like making Glop?

Do you love watching TV all day? — **NO** → Do you like playing pirates?

Do you love watching TV all day? — **Yes** → Do you think burping is funny?

Do you like playing pirates? — **YES** → Do you dream of playing in a tree house?

Do you like playing pirates? — **NO** → Do you like listening to very loud music?

Do you dream of playing in a tree house? — **YES** → Do you like making Glop?

Do you dream of playing in a tree house? — **NO** → Do you like playing at schools?

Do you like making Glop? — **Yes** → Do you like playing at schools?

Do you like making Glop? — **NO** → Do you enjoy nature walks?

Do you think burping is funny? — **Yes** → Do you like listening to very loud music?

Do you think burping is funny? — **No** → Do you hate fruit and vegetables?

Do you like listening to very loud music? — **YES** → Do you like playing at schools?

Do you like listening to very loud music? — **NO** → Do you like doing chores for your parents?

Do you like playing at schools? — **YES** → Do you like doing chores for your parents?

Do you like playing at schools? — **NO** → Do you enjoy nature walks?

Do you enjoy nature walks? — **NO** → Do you like doing chores for your parents?

Do you enjoy nature walks? — **Yes** → Could you put up with a grumpy friend?

Do you hate fruit and vegetables? — **NO** → Do you like doing chores for your parents?

Do you hate fruit and vegetables? — **Yes** → Do you like rude and horrid people?

Do you like doing chores for your parents? — **NO** → Do you like rude and horrid people?

Do you like doing chores for your parents? — **Yes** → Could you put up with a grumpy friend?

Could you put up with a grumpy friend? — **Yes** → Are you happy to be bossed about?

Could you put up with a grumpy friend? — **No** → Do you like goody-goodies?

Do you like rude and horrid people? — **NO** → Are you happy to be bossed about?

Do you like rude and horrid people? — **Yes** → Your best friend is **HORRID HENRY**

Are you happy to be bossed about? — **NO** → Do you like rude and horrid people?

Are you happy to be bossed about? — **NO** → Do you like goody-goodies?

Are you happy to be bossed about? — **Yes** → Your best friend is **MOODY MARGARET**

Do you like goody-goodies? — **NO** → Are you happy to be bossed about?

Do you like goody-goodies? — **Yes** → Your best friend is **PERFECT PETER**

Your best friend is HORRID HENRY

Your best friend is MOODY MARGARET

Your best friend is PERFECT PETER

Moody Margaret's Minty Mice

Christmas is coming, and Moody Margaret makes some Minty Mice to sweeten up her best friend, Sour Susan.

You will need

1 egg white
340g (12 oz) icing sugar
Chocolate chips
Unsalted peanut halves
Peppermint essence
Red liquorice laces

Instructions

1. Put the egg white into a big mixing bowl and whisk until it looks frothy.

2. Stir in the icing sugar. The mixture will turn into a dough, a bit like pastry.

3. Sprinkle a few drops of peppermint essence on the dough and knead with your hands so it's evenly mixed.

4. Divide the dough into eight pieces and shape each piece into a mouse shape, with one rounded end and one pointed end for the nose.

5. Use the chocolate chips for eyes, and push in the peanut halves to make the ears. Cut small pieces of the liquorice laces for the tails, and push them into the rounded ends of your mice.

Squeak! Squeak!

Christmas Star Puzzle

Show a friend the star diagram below and ask them to choose one of the names, without telling you who it is. Tell them that you are going to guess who they have chosen.

Now tell your friend that you are going to tap the names with a pencil, and ask them to spell the name of the character silently, one letter for each tap. When they reach the last letter tell them to shout 'stop'. Your pencil will be pointing to the correct name.

Don't tell your friend this! If you always put your pencil on the **START HERE** point, then tap in order on Margaret (tap 1), Al (tap 2), Sid (tap 3), Bert (tap 4) and so on, following the lines of the star, you'll always guess the right name.

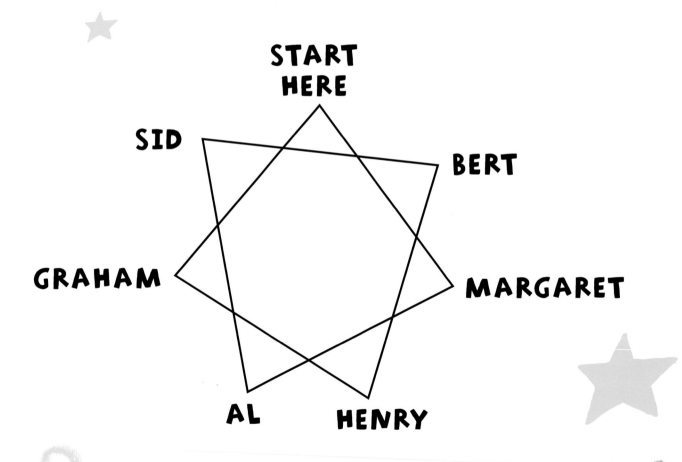

Henry's Guide to Staying Up Past Your Bedtime on Christmas Eve

I've <u>got</u> to stay up late on Christmas Eve so I can sneak up on Father Christmas and make sure I get all the presents on my list, <u>and</u> tell him that smelly socks and soggy satsumas are NOT presents. Here are my top tips for staying up late:

- I take a very long time getting ready for bed by brushing every tooth in my mouth, and washing every part of my body – at least twice. Then I ask Mum, very politely, to iron my pyjamas because they're creased. She can't complain because she's always nagging me to be clean and tidy, like wibble pants Perfect Peter.

- I go downstairs for a drink of water – as many times as I dare. If Mum and Dad get annoyed, I explain that I want to be healthy and water is very good for me. They have to agree because they're always telling me not to drink so much fizzywizz.

- I turn all the clocks in the house back a couple of hours, so that Mum and Dad think it's much earlier. Tee hee!

- I start talking to Dad about something really boring that I know he's interested in. Once he gets started, I know I'll be up for hours!

- If my mean, horrible parents force me to go to bed, I get up in the night and pretend to be sleepwalking. I keep my eyes open so that I don't bump into things, but I stare in a strange scary way.

If none of those things work…

- I hide behind the sofa until everyone else has gone to bed.

Henry

Horrid Henry's Christmas Quiz

Horrid Henry knows all about Christmas. It means starring in the School Play and getting lots and lots of presents! But how much do you know about Horrid Henry's Christmas?

1. Who does Miss Battle-Axe choose to play Mary in the School Christmas Play?

(a) Gorgeous Gurinder

(b) Moody Margaret

(c) Singing Soraya

2. When Henry misbehaves, which part does Miss Battle-Axe threaten to give him?

(a) Hind legs of a donkey

(b) Blade of grass

(c) Mary

3. Horrid Henry doesn't want a fairy on top of the Christmas tree. What does he want instead?

(a) Perfect Peter

(b) Mr Kill

(c) Terminator Gladiator

4. Who received this poem from Henry as their Christmas present?

Dear Old baldy ▬
Don't be sad
Be glad
Because you've had...
A very merry Christmas
Love from your lad,
Henry

(a) Dad

(b) Granddad

(c) Rich-Aunt Ruby

5. Why does Henry set an ambush for Father Christmas?

(a) To tell him not to give Perfect Peter any presents

(b) So he can rummage in his sack and find all the best presents

(c) To tell him very firmly that satsumas are NOT presents!

6. What does Henry think of these presents?
Match the correct answers and score one point for each:

a. Dictionary

b. £15.00

c. Pink bow tie

d. Huge tin
   of chocolates

e. Terminator Gladiator trident

1. Hurray!

2. Yuck!

3. OK - should have
   been a lot more

4. Eew

5. Yum

How did you do?

Check the answers on page 75.

8 – 10

Hallelujah! You've done so brilliantly, you could have spent
every Christmas with Horrid Henry!

5 – 7

Well done! You've got a pretty good idea of what goes on at
Christmas in Horrid Henry's household.

3 – 4

You're obviously having such a good time at Christmas, you
can't keep up with what happens at Horrid Henry's house.

1 – 2

Uh oh, it looks like you need to add 'Horrid Henry's Christmas
Cracker' to your Father Christmas list!

Christmas Present Wordsearch

Find the presents Henry gets at Christmas and some of the presents he *wanted* to get. Write the leftover letters in the spaces below, going from left to right along each row, to uncover a hidden message.

HANKIES
DICTIONARY
CARDIGAN
SATSUMAS
VESTS
JIGSAW

GOOSHOOTER
SWEETS
CHOCOLATE
SLIME
DINOSAUR
SUPERSOAKER

R	K	C	I	E	S	N	H	G	Y	H
N	E	E	H	T	M	A	N	R	R	R
A	Y	K	S	O	N	I	A	T	E	H
G	S	E	A	K	C	N	L	T	E	D
I	V	A	I	O	O	O	O	S	I	H
D	S	E	T	I	S	O	L	N	O	J
R	S	W	T	S	H	R	O	A	I	R
A	R	C	E	S	U	S	E	G	T	I
C	I	B	O	E	A	M	S	P	L	E
D	E	O	R	U	T	A	A	U	U	L
E	G	S	R	O	W	S	K	S	!	S

Look up, down, forwards, backwards and diagonally.

Hidden Message

_ _

_ _ _ _ _ _ _ _ _ _ _ _ _ _

Puzzle Answers

There are **12** slices of pizza hidden in the Annual.

Page 22
Horrid Henry Tricks
Stuck-up Steve
The five missing objects are:

1. Goo-Shooter
2. Gizmo
3. Red racing car
4. Supersoaker
5. Boomerang

Page 27
Nasty Nature Crossword

Page 35
Survival Criss-cross

Page 36
The Big Summer Quiz

1. (a)
2. (c)
3. (b)
4. (b)
5. (c)
6. (a)
7. (b)
8. (a)

Page 38
Perfect Peter's
Perplexing Puzzles
They are all exactly the same!

Page 52
Autumn Crossword

Page 55
Big Scary Phobias Wordsearch

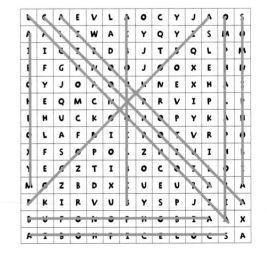

Page 57

Spooky Jokes Criss-cross

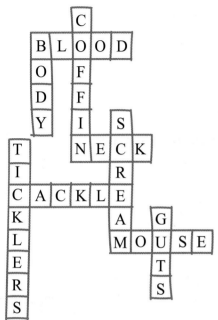

Page 61

Brainy Brian's Cross-out
Riddle-me-ree

The hairiest side of a cat is:
THE OUTSIDE

Page 65

Spot the Difference

The differences are:

1. The handle is missing from the cupboard door
2. The candle on the tree is red.
3. The stripe is missing from Henry's T-shirt sleeve.
4. The bauble in the box is red.
5. Perfect Peter's eyebrows are missing.
6. One of the Christmas tree branches is missing.

Page 70

Horrid Henry's
Christmas Quiz

1. (b)
2. (a)
3. (c)
4. (a)
5. (b)
6. a=2; b=3; c=4; d=5; e=1

Page 72

Christmas Present Wordsearch

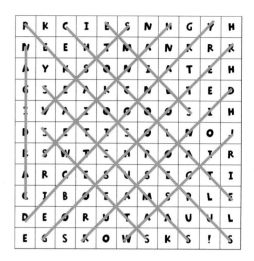

The hidden message is:
KING HENRY THE
HORRIBLE RULES OK!

You can read these other *Horrid Henry* titles, stories available as audio editions, read by Miranda Richardson

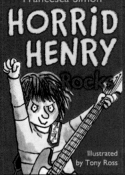

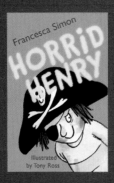

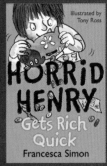

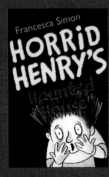

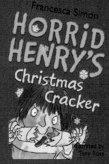

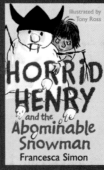

FRANCESCA SIMON

HORRID HENRY'S BIG BAD BOOK

Ten favourite stories – and more!

Illustrated by Tony Ross

FRANCESCA SIMON

HORRID HENRY'S WICKED WAYS

Illustrated by Tony Ross

Ten favourite stories – and more!

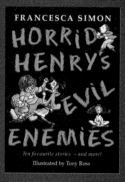

FRANCESCA SIMON

HORRID HENRY'S EVIL ENEMIES

Ten favourite stories – and more!

Illustrated by Tony Ross

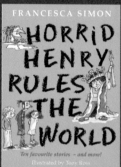

FRANCESCA SIMON

HORRID HENRY RULES THE WORLD

Ten favourite stories – and more!

Illustrated by Tony Ross

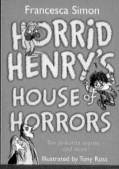

Francesca Simon

HORRID HENRY'S HOUSE of HORRORS

Ten favourite stories – and more!

Illustrated by Tony Ross

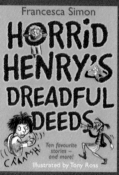

Francesca Simon

HORRID HENRY'S DREADFUL DEEDS

Ten favourite stories – and more!

Illustrated by Tony Ross

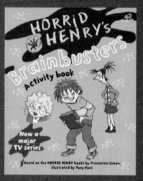

HORRID HENRY'S Brainbusters Activity book

Now a major TV series

Based on the HORRID HENRY books by Francesca Simon, illustrated by Tony Ross

HORRID HENRY'S Headscratchers Activity book

Now a major TV series

Based on the HORRID HENRY books by Francesca Simon, illustrated by Tony Ross

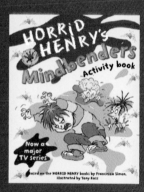

HORRID HENRY'S Mindbenders Activity book

Now a major TV series

Based on the HORRID HENRY books by Francesca Simon, illustrated by Tony Ross

HORRID HENRY'S Colouring Book

Now a major TV series

Based on the HORRID HENRY books by Francesca Simon, illustrated by Tony Ross

HOR H Puzz

Now a major TV series

Based on the HORRID HENRY

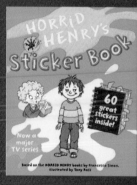

HORRID HENRY'S Sticker Book

60 great stickers inside!

Now a major TV series

Based on the HORRID HENRY books by Francesca Simon, illustrated by Tony Ross

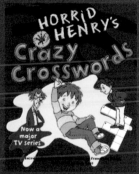

HORRID HENRY'S Crazy Crosswords

Now a major TV series

HORRID HENRY'S Mad Mazes

Now a major TV series

Based on the HORRID HENRY books by Francesca Simon, illustrated by Tony Ross

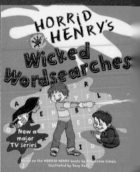

HORRID HENRY'S Wicked Wordsearches

Now a major TV series

Based on the HORRID HENRY books by Francesca Simon, illustrated by Tony Ross

HORRID HENRY'S Bumper fun Book

Now a major TV series

Based on the HORRID HENRY books by Francesca Simon, illustrated by Tony Ross

HORRID HENRY'S Classroom Chaos Activity book

Now a major TV series

Based on the HORRID HENRY books by Francesca Simon, illustrated by Tony Ross

HORRID HENRY'S Holiday Havoc Activity book

Now a major TV series

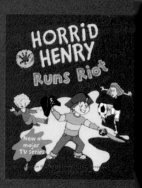

HORRID HENRY Runs Riot

Now a major TV series